THE CASE OF

TOXIC
TROUSERS

BY
CLIVE GIFFORD

Illustrated by Jane Cope

*Hodder
Children's
Books*

a division of Hodder Headline plc

First published in 1996 by Hodder Children's Books

The right of Clive Gifford and Jane Cope to be identified as the author and illustrator of this work has been asserted by them in accordance with the Copyright, Designs and Patents Act 1988.

Edited by Kay Barnham

Designed by Don Martin

10 9 8 7 6 5 4 3 2 1

A catalogue record for this book is available from the British Library.

ISBN 0 340 65596 8

Hodder Children's Books
A division of Hodder Headline plc
338 Euston Road
London NW1 3BH

Printed and bound by Cox & Wyman Ltd, Reading, Berks

HOW TO PLAY

It's pretty simple to follow the rules, the hard thing is completing the adventure successfully!

123 Each action or event has a number like this at its start. At the end of each event you will be told what to do next. Sometimes, you will just be told to turn to another numbered section. Sometimes, you will be given a choice of actions to take, each with a number you must turn to. Follow the instructions in the bold text and don't read any other sections on the way. Why? Because, that's cheating (see below).

You will start with some objects on your mission list. As you gain items, you must add them to your list. When you lose or trade items, you must cross them off your list. Your mission list is shown on the back page of the book. The bold writing at the end of each event will tell you when you've gained or lost any objects.

CHEATING

There's no point in cheating for three very important reasons. One, you won't have any fun playing the adventure again. Two, you won't be able to tell your friends truthfully that you completed the adventure. Three (and most important of all) Biceps Man and his superhero friends simply can't stand cheating. After all, baddies try to win by lying and cheating, so how can you be on their side if you are guilty of the same? And I can't even begin to tell you what superheroes do to cheats ...

Turn to Section 1 and Good Luck.

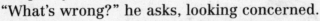

1 You finish the last page of a naff comic. Frustrated and bored, you toss it down on to your bed.

"What a load of rubbish!" you exclaim just as your stepdad, Jim, walks past your bedroom.

"What's wrong?" he asks, looking concerned.

"Oh nothing," you say. "Thank you for my birthday presents." You pick up and wave the two comics, forcing a smile.

"I'm sorry that we couldn't get you what you really wanted," says Jim looking a bit unhappy. "You know how difficult things are at the moment." You nod and Jim disappears into the bathroom.

It was your birthday yesterday. You'd hoped for a mountain bike, if not as good as Colin's, then one like Rob's or Satinda's. Instead, you got two of these rubbishy comics, *Death Cave* and *Fist of Fear*, both featuring an unimpressive hero called Biceps Man.

But it's certainly not the fault of Jim and your mum. It's the fault of whoever or whatever has tampered with the reservoir that supplies Eldon Valley and Eldon Village with water.

It all started a few weeks ago when strange bubbly water started coming out of the taps of all the houses in the village. The water board was called and traced the problem to the reservoir at the far end of the valley.

Go to 26.

2 A little later, on the other side of town, three scruffy teenagers are holding a trial.

"So the case for the prosecution concludes by saying that Eric told his parents that it was the Eco Warriors that broke into the ToxCo complex."

"But..." Eric starts to protest, but is interrupted by the bossy teenager sitting on the log. "As I was saying, the result of this is that we're all in big trouble at college."

"I'm really sorry everyone," says Eric, "I am, George, I really am."

"It's not George, it's Defender, you idiot Eric!"

"How come I'm now Eric, but you're still called Defender?"

"Simple, you're no longer an Eco Warrior."

"But the verdict hasn't been reached!"

"Oh it will be in a moment."

"Must we do this? It's so silly," moans a tall, thin boy.

"Of course we must, Earthwatcher," snaps Defender. "I declare Eric guilty of crimes against the Earth, and I..."

Just as Defender is about to pass sentence, Stargazer startles them all.

"Sorry I'm late everyone, I got talking to a very interesting young kid in Bridge Street."

"Young kids aren't interesting," growls Defender.

"Oh, this one is. I think we should hand over our information and let this child handle it."

"Are you joking?"

"Well, we're leaving for Swallowtown College on Monday after the school fête, so there's not much we can do after then, is there?"

"Stargazer's got a point," agrees Earthwatcher.

"I don't know," says Defender. "I want to meet this kid first."

Go to 28.

3 Mrs Patel, Satinda's mother, is running the memory game stall. You hand her your last 20p and she explains the rules.

"I'm going to show you a picture for 20 seconds. Then, I'll show you a second picture for the same length of time. You have to work out which objects are missing in the second picture. OK?" You nod.

Go to 102.

4 Rob giggles as you join the queue for the school trip. You're immediately behind Colin the Computer Whizz and Sandra Lockwood, the school swot.

"Didn't expect to see you on this sort of trip," says Mr Hapless, surprised. "Here you go," he adds, handing you a special note.

You go to join Rob out in the playground but he won't stop teasing you.

"What a nerd! What a geek!" he chants so you leave him and get changed early for gym class.

Add school trip note and go to 42.

5 Before you can answer, the starting pistol goes "bang!" and off go five teachers and eleven parents in old potato sacks. The obstacle course starts with a sack race, followed by rows of tables and tunnels, and finishes with a 50-metre sprint to a winning tape held by Ms Sharp and the plump mayoress.

The course is well-designed, but it's nowhere near as much fun as previous years which had water obstacles. Mr Grim, elbowing Mr Hapless to the floor for his comment over the speaker system, soon takes an early lead.

"What a surprise," you comment sarcastically to Rob.

Halfway through the tables and tunnels section and Mr Grim is way out in front.

"It's the same every year," you hear a parent sigh behind you.

The gorilla who left the comics earlier is wandering along the edge of the track near the

finish line. Everyone is laughing so much at Mr
Hapless still struggling in his potato sack, that they
don't notice the gorilla sidle up to the track and
secretly drop a banana skin on to the ground.

Go to 104.

6 You spend the whole of the morning
wandering around the village, searching for
clues. Apart from bumping into your schoolfriends,
Rob and Carol, and crossing the road to avoid
Spencer Stimson, the school bully, nothing much
happens.

Every time you meet an adult and ask them if
they know anything about the strange water, they
look at you oddly or in an annoyed sort of way.

It's nearly lunchtime and you're hungry.

Do you head over to the library (go to 47)?
**Do you head over to the _Eldon Gazette_ (go to
10)?**
Do you head back home for lunch (go to 54)?

7 "Oh, the gorilla. That's one of those drama students from Swallowtown. They're looking after the supermonsters stall. Ms Sharp was very excited about that stall. I think she's hoping it will replace some of the excitement we normally get from the sponge throwing," replies Miss Jenkins.

Go to 49.

8 "Steve said in his letter that Toxic spilt some of the chemicals from the barrels on to his trousers. If you can get those trousers to the police, Eldon could possibly be saved."

"How come?" you ask, a little puzzled.

"Well, it's unlikely that the chemicals will wash out, so scientists could work out what the chemicals are and make an antidote. Plus, the police would be able to use them as evidence.

"The trousers are very similar to the ones in the window of the local dry cleaners, except they have red and yellow checks," says Dennis. "If you can get hold of the real trousers, Toxic's plan will fail, I'm sure."

"Why me?"

"You're Eldon's only chance. You're obviously a bright kid who can be trusted. Even Teddy Toxic wouldn't think twice about a child snooping around."

"Why can't you do anything?"

"Because Toxic is already watching me. He's suspicious of me and, remember, the paper's photographer has already disappeared."

"Haven't you told the police?"

"Of course I have, but they don't believe me. Oh crikey," says Doug Dennis, his ears pricking up. "I've got to go. I'm in hiding for a few days."

You gulp. When a journalist as fearless as Doug 'Deadline' Dennis – the man who actually asked the enormous mayoress her dress size – is scared, you know there must be a good reason.

You look up to ask another question but Doug Dennis has disappeared. Just ahead you can see a bright white jeep with lots of extra headlights, roaring along at twice the speed limit. The number plate TOX 1C tells you exactly who it is.

There's a blue floppy disk on the floor in front of you. Doug Dennis must have dropped it when he fled.

Do you pick it up (go to 44) or not (go to 30)?

9 "Correct!" beams Mrs Patel. "Here's your prize," she says, handing you a fluffy pink teddy bear. You thank her politely and leave the memory game stall.

Add the teddy bear to your list and go to 135.

10 You go to the ramshackle old building that houses the offices of the *Eldon Gazette*. It's locked and there's a sign on the door. "Gone away for a long holiday. Don't know when I'll be back – Doug Dennis, Editor, *Eldon Gazette*."

That's really strange. The village is in the middle of its biggest crisis ever and its one journalist goes on a holiday rather than investigating.

Go to 54.

11 Something, thankfully, seems to be happening in the playground. A few of the parents and kids are rushing over to a figure in a white t-shirt and horrible patterned trousers. From where you are standing you can see that the small crowd is slowly making its way towards you.

By the time you spot who the figure is, most of the crowd has drifted away. Now you can see what all the fuss is about. Teddy Toxic has turned up at your school fête. "Grrrr. Him of all people," you growl.

"Now, now. I've never met him but I've heard that Mr Toxic has been very generous to the village in the past," tuts Miss Jenkins. "Make sure you're polite to him."

Toxic appears in front of your stall.

"Mr Toxic, how pleasant to see you," gushes Miss Jenkins. Teddy Toxic ignores her.

"Yeah, like I uh, am, uh looking for an old Biceps Man comic for my, uh, nephew, uh, know what I mean?"

"We haven't got any," you scowl.

"Oh, I think we have," interrupts Miss Jenkins.

"We just had some handed in a minute ago," she says picking them up and laying them out in front of Teddy Toxic.

If you bought issue 219, go to 117, otherwise, go to 60.

12 If only you'd paid more attention! You spend the next few days searching for the stranger but he or she is nowhere to be seen. Your school fête passes uneventfully and a couple of weeks later, everyone, including your family, starts moving out of Eldon.

THE END

13 "Hello. Would you sign a petition against Teddy Toxic?"

"Who are you?"you ask.

"I'm Cathy, whoops, I mean Stargazer. Forget the name Cathy, Defender would be angry with me if he knew I'd let it slip."

"OK, Stargazer," you sigh, "what's this all about?"

"I shouldn't really tell you this but I'm an Eco Warrior. I go to the Swallowtown Drama College, but I'm part of a gang pledged to stop damage to our planet and our children."

"Oh really?" you say with interest. "So why are you against Teddy Toxic?"

"Well, Toxic has a long record of damaging the countryside. He's well-known for ruthlessly cutting down trees and building factories on nature reserves protected by law."

"If they're protected by law, how does he get away with it?"

"Oh, he's very clever. He usually buys the land cheaply because of some misfortune or other."

You think about the Biceps Man comic again. "Like a water supply that's been meddled with?" you blurt out loud.

"We hadn't thought of that. No, surely he wouldn't do that here on his own doorstep." Stargazer seems surprised.

Suddenly, your stepdad pipes up from the lounge, "Who's at the door?"

Do you say an "Eco Warrior" (go to 41)?
Do you say "someone selling encyclopedias" (go to 63)?

14 The people of Eldon are collecting all the rainwater they can but with summer approaching and the weather forecasters predicting little rain, everyone fears for the flowers and trees of Eldon which have already started to wilt.

Staring out of your window, you'd rather not think about what the valley will look like if a solution to the water problem isn't found soon.

Your mum and Jim are talking of having to move out of Eldon to a horrible big town miles away from all of your friends. You like it here very much and don't want to leave, but the cost of all that expensive bottled water is becoming too hard for most families, including yours. That's why mum and Jim couldn't afford to buy you a proper birthday present.

None of the adults in Eldon seem to be able to do anything about it. The Police are baffled and although the scientists keep treating the water, it doesn't seem to do any good. All the mayoress of Eldon has been able to do is offer a £10,000 reward from the village funds for anyone who can solve the mystery.

You're determined to find out who is behind all of this. If you can find out who or what it is, then hopefully, the strange fizzy water will stop and life will return to normal.

You look around your room for inspiration. Your eyes rest on the two comics on your bed. Huh! Biceps Man wouldn't have a clue what to do. Anything that doesn't require a hefty punch is completely beyond him.

You open the second comic, *Death Cave*, almost at the end of an adventure where Biceps Man is searching for his missing partner, She-Minx.

You can't face any more Biceps Man adventures and wander downstairs into the kitchen. The radio is blaring and your stepdad, Jim, is cooking one of his awful, greasy fry-ups.

"Listen to this," he shouts over the racket. "Now that's what I call music," he declares. You pour yourself a bowl of cereal just as the scratchy blast of noise comes to an end.

"That was a real rave from the grave there – Teddy Toxic and His Toxettes with Fast Car Fury. I remember his terrible, *Never Mind The Toxic* comeback tour. Yeah! Where is he now, eh? Wow!

Listen! It's top of the hour and here's the traffic news with Iona Porsche, Hey Iona, how's it going?..."

Your stepdad switches the radio off.

"There won't be anything as good as that on for hours," he says seriously. Despite his earring, Jim can be so uncool at times.

As your stepdad continues his fry-up, you ponder what you've just read in the Biceps Man comic. The rainwater in *Death Cave* was poisoned so that evil Drakor Thumb-Twister could buy the whole kingdom of Naturia for next to nothing. You start to get excited. Could something similar be going on in Eldon? It sounds unlikely, but you must start investigating at once.

"Hey, don't you want any breakfast?" Jim asks, as you put your trainers on and grab a jacket.

"No, I'm fine. I've got a lot of work to do," you reply excitedly, rushing out of the back door. The future of Eldon can't wait for your breakfast.

Go to 6.

15 "I sent back the pair which we couldn't clean. I think I have the other ones here," the dry cleaning lady continues.

She rummages around in a back room before coming back out with the strangest trousers you've ever seen.

Go to 56.

16 A couple of days pass by without any excitement until Spencer Stimson corners you one break time. With Mr Hapless away on the school trip, there's no teacher on break duty. So when Spencer offers you two choices (handing over your geography homework or getting beaten up) you decide to give him your homework and endure a detention for not handing it in yourself.

Go to 151.

17 You wander slowly through the small village market over to the newspaper seller, Gary. He looks very glum.

"Sorry, kid – I've no papers to sell. It looks like Steve and Doug, who run the paper, have disappeared."

"Thanks," you say and wander back through the market, stopping for a while to gaze at the new mountain bike in one of the shop windows.

Go to 36.

18 If you thought the white pencil was missing, go to 9.
If you thought anything else was missing, go to 106.

19 Back at home, your mind is spinning with all the new information and clues you've collected.

If you have issue 219 of *Biceps Man* comic, go to 65. If not, go to 31.

20 What do you want to do?

If you want to continue reading your pop magazine, *WOW!*, go to 50.
If you want to look at the leaflet Stargazer gave you, go to 33.
If you want to look at the *Swallowtown Echo*, go to 57.

21 On the other side of the village, a little later, the Eco Warriors are meeting at George Grim's house.

"Well I'm pleased your temper tantrum stopped you passing information to that poor child," scowls Stargazer. "I'm having second thoughts about getting someone younger than us involved."

"Don't be stupid. We can contact that kid at his school fête tomorrow," declares Defender.

"Why are we using a kid to do our dangerous work?" asks Earthwatcher.

"Because our glorious leader here is too scared of his Dad," cries Stargazer.

"What do you mean? We tried to break into Teddy Toxic's offices," snaps Defender.

"Yes, but we bungled it, didn't we and we may even get expelled because of it," insists Stargazer.

"It's too late for us to do anything now," points out Earthwatcher. "So why argue? We have to be back at school on Monday and that's that."

"So let's just make sure the kid is at the school

fête," says Defender, switching on his father's computer and starting to type out a letter.

Go to 84.

22 A little later, Miss Jenkins give you time off to have a look around. You're still annoyed by your first-ever meeting with Teddy Toxic and decide to take out your anger on the popular Punch-a-Teacher stall. As much as some kids would like it to be a real one, the 'teacher' is just an inflatable dummy linked to a weighing machine which judges how hard you can hit it.

You've never made it beyond the Complete Wimp rating before, but you're so angry that this time you manage Young Boxer. Mr Grim, in charge of the machine, looks impressed.

"We'll have to channel your new-found strength into your gym work," he says with a grin. Rats. So now, you'll be given even more work to do in the gym. Your mood grows blacker and blacker.

Wandering further, you turn out your pockets and find yourself down to your last 20p. You don't notice Godzilla's note fluttering out of your pocket on to the ground by your feet. Your 20p will pay for you to have a go on one of three different stalls: the memory game, the coconut shy and the fortune teller, Mystic Mary.

Cross the Dinosaur note off your list.
If you choose Mystic Mary, go to 125.
If you choose the memory game, go to 3.
If you choose the coconut shy, go to 39.

23 You walk into the police station, where you spot Inspector Marchbank and two frizzy-haired policemen. They all look very tired, no doubt because of their 'round the clock' efforts to solve the water mystery.

"I was wondering about the water problem," you say.

"So was I," Inspector Marchbank replies in irritation. "I'm also wondering how I convince these two to have their new frizzy hair shaved off so that they can get their helmets back on," the Inspector says fiercely.

"Run along and stop wasting police time." Inspector Marchbank points you towards the door.

Go to 36.

24 "I'm afraid they've just been sent back to their owner. One pair was lovely and clean, but we just couldn't shift the funny stains on the other pair."

You look very disappointed.

"You should have been here a few moments ago. They were quite a sight, I can tell you," the lady says.

"Can you remember whether the stained pair had cars or stars?" you ask urgently.

"Now the black and purple checks had the stars… or was it the cars. Do you know, I'm not sure. We see so many pairs of trousers in this place, that I really don't know."

You thank the lady for her help and leave.

Go to 56.

25 There are lots of pages torn out of this naff old annual but one feature catches your eye.

TOXICTASTIC!

the new Punk movement that's worrying parents so much. But we here at Pop-Tastic say 'Go for it' Teddy.

His latest single available on both 7" and 12" formats is called Fast Car Fury and their new long-player, Classroom Revolt, is out shortly.

The future of pop music isn't healthy, it's poisonous. Toxic, in fact. Teddy Toxic and his groovesome backing band, The Toxettes, are taking over the music world with their crazy sound. Some call it revolutionary, others call it a right racket, but one thing it most definitely is, is LOUD. That's right kids, L-O-U-D! Teddy Toxic and the Toxettes are part of

Go to 11.

26 The bubbly water seemed fine at first but its effects soon became obvious. The bubbles made everyone burp all the time and as for people's hair... You can't help smiling at the memory of last week's trip to the High Street.

When baths were banned, you weren't bothered too much, but when the water board closed the swimming pool and the school goldfish died, you realized that this was a serious problem. And as for Mrs Merton's washing... She wasn't very amused when all her clothes dissolved!

Go to 14.

27 Have you worked out what's missing then?" Mrs Patel asks.

Make a decision and write down your answer. Cross off the money from your list and then go to 18.

28 You decide to head out into the village. You can't help noticing how much quieter it is than usual. It looks as if even more people are moving away from Swallowtown.

Go to 36.

29 You trudge to school the next morning dressed up in your school uniform. Fancy having to wear your uniform on a Saturday – as if five days a week isn't enough! Miss Jenkins greets you in the school playground. "You volunteered for the book stall again, how wonderful," she squeals. She's a small, thin lady with the biggest, thickest glasses you've ever seen.

You start humping some of the books on to the stall's wooden tables. At least the weather is dry and sunny, but it is a whole day wasted from your toxic trousers investigation.

Go to 98.

30 You walk through the village, your head swimming with Doug Dennis's news.

If you decide to open the file Doug Dennis gave you, go to 87.
If you decide to head for the dry cleaners to look for the trousers, go to 58.

31 The day after the fête, you go with Jim to a car boot sale in Swallowtown and then return home for lunch.

All through the day you think about all the weird things that have happened. That evening, your mum walks in with the *Swallowtown Echo*, the closest thing to a local paper now that the *Eldon Gazette* has stopped and Doug Dennis has disappeared.

"Where's Jim?" you ask.

"Oh, flushed with his success in the obstacle race, he's decided to burn all the garden rubbish he's been planning to get rid of for ages," replies your mum. "I've got to get some more bottled water," she sighs. "Will you be all right?" You nod. She doesn't know how much you've got to think about.

Go to 45.

32 Back at school the next day, you are edgy waiting for a response from Teddy Toxic. You find it hard to concentrate in lessons and get several tellings-off.

"Are you OK?" asks your friend, Rob.

"Yeah, fine," you say unconvincingly.

"Don't worry, you've got your wonderful trip to the exciting ToxCo complex to look forward to!" he jokes. You smile weakly.

Go to 149.

33

BAN TOXIC'S PRODUCTS

Teddy Toxic owns ToxCo, a company connected with shady organisations. Its environmental track record is terrible.

Worse, ToxCo produced the anti-ecology computer game, Toxman the Eco-Basher which many have called the nastiest computer game ever. Although the game may be banned soon, we want further action. March against ToxCo. Don't buy ToxCo products. Shun Teddy Toxic in public.

Go to 20.

34 Go to 144.

35

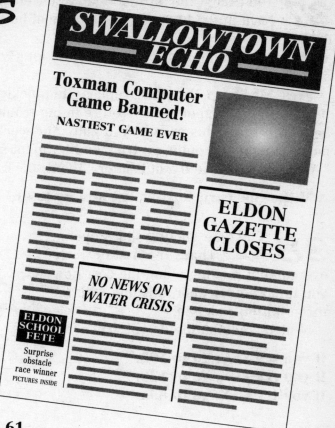

SWALLOWTOWN ECHO

Toxman Computer Game Banned!

NASTIEST GAME EVER

ELDON GAZETTE CLOSES

NO NEWS ON WATER CRISIS

ELDON SCHOOL FETE

Surprise obstacle race winner
PICTURES INSIDE

Go to 61.

36 You reach the centre of the village. Where do you want to go now?

If you want to walk to the newsagent's, go to 67.

If you would like to head for the newspaper stand at the market, go to 17.

If you want to pay a visit to the police station, go to 23.

37 You accept the dare and jab Spencer quite hard in the back. "Ow!" the school bully exclaims.

"Stimson!" Ms Sharp shouts. "See me after assembly."

"Yes, Ms Sharp," Spencer replies. He quickly turns round and spots you. "You're in big trouble," he growls under his breath. You gulp. Spencer's never caught you pulling a trick on him before. "Well done," says Rob a little later. "Here's the card."

Add the tips card to your list and go to 46.

38 The door silently slides open. Great! That's the first obstacle overcome. Creeping along the corridor, you find another door, this one with a three-button codepad.

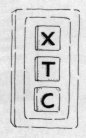

Which combination do you try?

If you try TXC, go to 103.
If you try TCX, go to 128.
If you try CTX, go to 85.

39 You pay up your last 20p and Mrs Kengrove, Rob's mum, hands you three wooden balls. You take careful aim and throw hard at the coconuts but you miss with all three attempts. This seems to be typical of your luck at the moment.

Cross the money off your list and go to 135.

40 Just as you leave the house for school, your stepdad calls you back.

"There's a phone call for you. The voice sounds ever so familiar," says Jim. You pick up the phone and nearly faint. It's Teddy Toxic.

"I got your message. Look, I've got a lot of, like, wild trousers. That's one of the, uh, ways I made my name in music. Toxic's trousers were as, uh, famous as anyone's a few years ago. Now, which pair are you after?"

If you ask for the pair with red and yellow checks with stars, go to 72.
If you ask for the pair with yellow and red checks with cars, go to 144.
If you ask for the pair with purple and green checks with stars, go to 34.

41 "An Eco Warrior? Don't talk to me about Eco Warriors," Jim shouts as he rushes out into the hall. "I heard about your lot breaking into the ToxCo Complex. I thought you were being sent to borstal or something."

Stargazer goes to protest but your stepdad slams the door in her face.

"You shouldn't talk to those Eco Warriors. They're a bunch of teenage layabouts," says Jim.

"But she was saying that Teddy Toxic does bad things to the countryside."

"I don't know anything about that. I just know that I like some of his old records and he's made a very generous offer to all the people in Eldon."

"It's only half the price of the house," adds your mum quietly.

"Still, it's better than nothing, which is precisely what this place is worth with no decent water," your stepdad replies.

Go to 20.

42 After changing into your P.E. kit, you line up with the rest of the class for your gym lesson. You quite enjoy gym, except for vaults. Still, today's lesson should be all right, as you're all going to be doing floorwork. You like doing forward and backward rolls and you're easily the best in your class at handstands and cartwheels.

Mr Grim walks in front of your class. Everyone jokes about how he acts like a sergeant major in the army. Of course, they joke in the playground or after school. No one ever dares to say anything in front of him. This is because any word, any smile, or any movement results in fifty press-ups.

Mr Grim barks at everyone to begin with some forward rolls. Just as you start to lean down, he grabs your shoulder.

"Everyone except you. I'd like you to practise jumping over the vaulting horse instead." You groan and some of your classmates start sniggering. Everyone knows you loathe doing vaults.

Go to 90.

43 You're already at the back of the group. If you're going to risk looking around the ToxCo complex by yourself, now may be your best chance. It's up to you. Should you creep away?

Do you creep out of the workshop now (go to 64) or not (go to 157)?

44 You pick the disk up and read the label. All it says is SG2 Code: 504. You pop the disk into your pocket.

Add the blue floppy disk to your list and go straight to 30.

45 What do you want to do next?
Do you want to look at the headlines of the *Swallowtown Echo* (go to 35)?
Do you want to watch the sports video (go to 142)?
If you've got the blue computer disk, do you want to check it on the computer (go to 200)?

46 Assembly finishes with Ms Sharp mentioning the school trip to the ToxCo complex. "Would anyone who wants to go on the trip, please line up in front of Mr Hapless."

You watch a couple of the school's nerds rush over to Mr Hapless. "Cor, what a bunch of geeks," exclaims Rob.

Do you line up to go on the ToxCo trip (go to 4) or not (go to 42)?

47 You wander into the library and start looking around aimlessly. You're not really sure what you're searching for.

Miss Snooty, the librarian walks up to you. "How can I help?" she asks, peering over the top of her horn-rimmed glasses.

"Have you any books on water pollution?"

"We don't have many. Everyone's suddenly interested in that subject, as I'm sure you can imagine," the librarian sighs. "If any remain, they'll be in the second bookcase in the Teddy Toxic Wing over there.

"The Teddy Toxic wing?"

"Yes, Mr Toxic, the owner of ToxCo, generously donated enough money to repair part of the library, providing that we named it after him.

"Actually, I'm really interested in Teddy Toxic and his history too," you add hastily.

"Well, there's nothing on him here, I'm afraid. The only other condition Mr Toxic set was that we remove any reference to him from the library. He's a very private man, you see."

"So you had to remove all references apart from that big sign with his name on?" you chip in.

"Er, yes," replies the librarian.

Slightly confused, you thank Miss Snooty and head over to the local history section. An enormous picture of Teddy Toxic dominates the shelves of books. You flick through the couple of books on water pollution but they're really dull. You head for home.

From behind the thrillers shelves, a mysterious figure is watching you.

"So, this child is interested in Teddy Toxic too..."

Go to 54.

48 If you have a school trip note, go to 149. If not, go to 108.

49 Frowning with boredom, you watch the fête continue at its deadly slow pace. You sell the odd book and try to avoid the smirks and glances of your friends Rob and Satinda as well as the grin from bully, Spencer Stimson. "I bet he tricked me on to the stall," you think.

Go to 105.

50 You start flicking through *WOW!* and come to a page spoilt by lots of pen-marks. "Vandals!" you curse, but stare at the page more carefully, it looks like someone's doodled on purpose.

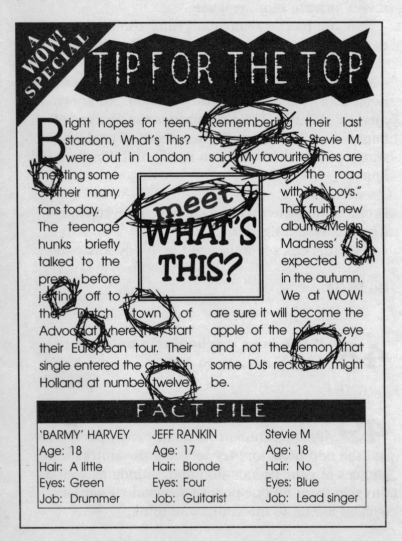

A WOW! SPECIAL

TIP FOR THE TOP

Bright hopes for teen stardom, What's This? were out in London meeting some of their many fans today. The teenage hunks briefly talked to the press before jetting off to the Dutch town of Advocaat where they start their European tour. Their single entered the charts in Holland at number twelve.

Remembering their last tour, lead singer Stevie M, said "My favourite times are on the road with the boys." Their fruity new album, 'Melon Madness' is expected out in the autumn. We at WOW! are sure it will become the apple of the public's eye and not the lemon that some DJs reckon it might be.

meet WHAT'S THIS?

FACT FILE

'BARMY' HARVEY	JEFF RANKIN	Stevie M
Age: 18	Age: 17	Age: 18
Hair: A little	Hair: Blonde	Hair: No
Eyes: Green	Eyes: Four	Eyes: Blue
Job: Drummer	Job: Guitarist	Job: Lead singer

Try to work out the message and then go to 2.

51 After a lengthy lecture on how to behave from Miss Jenkins, the stall stays quiet for another half an hour. Someone dressed up as the Godzilla dinosaur comes over to speak to you.

"I've already seen King Kong. I don't need you as well," you snap.

"But I've got a message for you," the badly-made dinosaur pleads. Godzilla opens its scaly paw clutching a small piece of paper. He whispers "When your stepdad wins the obstacle race, the prize will be very important."

Before you can ask any questions, Godzilla has lumbered off to battle King Kong once again on the supermonsters' stall.

Add the Dinosaur note to your list.
Do you want to look at the note now (go to 70)
or not (go to 22)?

52 The door refuses to budge but at least an alarm hasn't sounded. You're just about to try another combination when you're suddenly tapped on the shoulder.

Go to 164.

53 You skip over the carpet-tiles and rush into Teddy Toxic's private quarters. You try to explore, but as the alarm rings, doors seem to be sliding shut every way you turn.

Go to 175.

54 You arrive home to find a small package addressed to you but with no stamps on it.

"Someone from the village must have popped it through the letter box," says your mum.

You open the envelope to see the latest copy of *WOW!* magazine, your favourite pop mag. Why didn't it come through the post? You are very puzzled.

You are about to leaf through the magazine when the doorbell rings.

Go to 13.

55 Go to 52.

56 You start to walk back home when you hear a hissing sound coming from around the corner. You follow the noise, saying, "Doug Dennis, I thought you were leaving."

"I'm not Doug Dennis, I'm Defender," says a gangly teenager stepping out from behind the corner of the wall.

"What kind of name is that?" you smirk.

"It's a magnificent name. It's a name fit for a leader. I am the leader of the Eco Warriors," the teenager replies pompously.

"Oh, Cathy told me about you," you say.

"It's Stargazer, not Cathy. Honestly, how can we

work as an effective unit if we don't all stick to the rules and procedures?"

Defender sounds a little loopy.

Defender suddenly stops moaning and asks, "Do you like taking risks?"

"Well, I often pull tricks on the school bully, not that he ever realises," you reply.

"I mean *real* risks," insists Defender rudely. "You see I have lots of information for you about Teddy Toxic, though I'm not sure if it's worth giving to you, shorty," Defender snaps rudely.

"Well, I have lots of information about how Teddy Toxic is mucking around with Eldon's water, but if you think for one moment that I'm going to tell my secrets to someone so rude..." you snap back.

"Watch out kid," says Defender advancing towards you.

"George! Georgey-Porgey! Are you there?" the shrill voice of a woman cuts through the air.

Defender's face turns bright red. "Coming Mummy," he shouts back.

"Coming Mummy," you mimic.

Defender looks as if he's going to explode. The shrill voice turns into a shriek. "Georgey, if you don't come here this minute, I'll throw away your eggy soldiers."

"Eggy soldiers," you squeal with laughter.

"I'll show you not to mess with me. I may be a spoilt only child, but my parents, one of whom you know very well, will do anything for me," he splutters. "You'll be sorry you crossed me," he hisses.

Go to 62.

57 Apart from the article on the Eco Warriors, nothing much interests you in the paper. You put it down.

TEDDY TOXIC THROWS LIFELINE

Millionaire businessman, Teddy Toxic, has thrown a lifeline to many of the beleagured residents of crisis-stricken Eldon village. He has offered to buy up the whole of Eldon Valley despite its increasingly serious water problem.

Andrew Pudge of Vale Port Property Services explained last night that Toxic is offering only half, and sometimes as little as a quarter of the market price. But he maintained that it is a very good offer, in the circumstances, costing Toxic a lot of money.

TEENAGERS BREAK-IN

A small group of teenagers has been found to be responsible for the recent break-in at Teddy Toxic's ToxCo complex.

The self-styled Eco Warriors, many of them students at Swallowtown Drama College, owned up to the break-in, in which they caused some accidental damage.

Teddy Toxic was reported to be furious, not at the damage, which will be paid for by the students, but at the breach in his advanced security system. He is hoping to replace much of the system in a few weeks time.

Go to 20.

58 You reach the dry cleaners, but there's only a pair of grey suit trousers in the window.

"Hello there, how can I help you?" a small round woman with masses of curly hair smiles at you.

"Have you been drinking the fizzy tap water?" you ask.

"How dare you? I'm naturally curly and I always have my hair like this!" the lady exclaims.

"Sorry. I was wondering if you remembered a pair of brightly-checked trousers that you had in here recently," you ask.

"Oh yes, I remember both," she says proudly.

"Both of them?" you say, surprised.

"Yes, there were two pairs. One had cars in between the checks and one had stars," the lady replies.

If you have already read Doug Dennis's file on Teddy Toxic, go to 24, otherwise go to 15.

59 You make it to the door without a hitch and walk through.

Meanwhile, back near the computer workshops, Mr Hapless has spotted that you are missing. I'm ever so sorry," he apologises to the guide, "but one of my schoolchildren seems to have got lost."

"They're more likely to be snooping around," glares the guide. "If Mr Toxic finds out, we'll all be for the high jump," he warns, ushering the group back along some corridors and towards Toxic's personal offices.

Go to 141.

60 Toxic greedily grabs issue 219 and tucks it away inside his jacket. "Excellent," he smiles, his two gold teeth glinting in the sunlight.

"How much did I mark the comic up for?" Miss Jenkins asks you dreamily. "It costs £50," you reply. Miss Jenkins gives you a glare but Toxic says "Fair enough. In fact, uh, I'll double that as, uh, I'm stinking rich, ha, ha, ha."

"Oh thank you Mr Toxic," Miss Jenkins simpers.

"Consider it a donation to, uh, the school. Build a Teddy Toxic Memorial Wing or something."

"Maybe they should have a Teddy Toxic cell at the police station, as well," you scowl.

Miss Jenkins tells you off.

"I don't like your attitude," says Teddy. "Still, I got what I, uh, came for, thanks. Like, uh, see ya teach."

Go to 51.

61 The rest of Sunday evening drifts by uneventfully. Monday morning comes and it's back to school once more.

If you sent Teddy Toxic a note, go to 40.
If you didn't, go to 48.

62 You're back at school. "Enjoy your day off?" your friend Satinda asks.

"Yes, it was... interesting," you reply carefully.

"It's the only nice thing that's come out of this fizzy water crisis," chips in another of your friends, Rob Vernon. Everyone had the day off yesterday,

while plumbers fitted special water tanks at your school.

"Shhhh," Mr Hapless, your Maths teacher, puts his fingers to his lips and frowns. School assembly is about to start.

Ms Sharp, your school headmistress, drones on about the problems with the water. Finally, she mentions various other pieces of news about the school fête at the weekend.

"Do you know anything about the Toxman computer game?" you whisper to Rob. You know he reads all the computer magazines.

"Yeah, I've got a tips card about it right here, not that it's any use to me, I'm not allowed to play it," Rob replies.

"Shhh," hisses Mr Hapless.

"I'll let you have the tips card if you dare to get Spencer Stimson in trouble," says Rob with an evil glint in his eye. You look ahead. Spencer Stimson, the school bully, is standing right in front of you.

Do you trick Spencer (go to 37)?
Do you leave him alone (go to 46)?

63 "OK, tell him to go," shouts Jim from the dining room.

"Him? What a cheek," exclaims Stargazer with her hands on her hips. "Now what was I saying? Ah, yes. It's not only the damage Teddy Toxic does to the countryside, it's the damage he does to children's minds that we're worried about."

You look puzzled.

"Have you heard of his evil game, Toxman the Eco Buster?"

"Yes, but I've never played it. My parents would kill me if I did."

"Well, Teddy Toxic makes and distributes it. We're calling for it to be banned. Here's more information on it," Stargazer says, handing you a leaflet. "I'd better go. This petition is the last thing we can do before we go back to college. Thanks for your idea about Toxic meddling with the water."

"I... I didn't mean it, I just thought..." you stammer, but Stargazer, or Cathy, or whatever her name is, skips off down the road.

Go to 20.

64 You quietly shuffle out of the room and go back to the doorway you saw earlier. You try to force the door open but it refuses to budge. There's a codepad with three buttons. You heard the guide tap a button three times but which button was it?

If you press the triangle button, go to 38.
If you press the hexagon button, go to 55.
If you press the circle button, go to 52.

65 You flick through your new *Biceps Man* comic. Teddy Toxic seems to be the only person who loves them and he particularly wanted this issue. Perhaps he'll trade it for something? You hatch a plan and write out a short letter in your best handwriting.

> I have issue 219 of Biceps Man comic.
> I know it is very valuable. I'm not
> interested in money. I'm a big fan of punk
> music and fashion. I'm particularly
> interested in a pair of your wild trousers.
>
> A friend.

You pop the letter in the post-box and settle down that evening for some television and some boring homework.

Go to 31.

66 With all the alarms blaring, you race this way and that along narrow corridors. You can't believe your luck when you spot a doorway out of the building. You run towards it. Behind you, Teddy Toxic has recovered and has started giving chase. He's catching up, until he crashes into Mr Hapless, coming from a different direction.

Go to 158.

67 As you are heading towards the newsagent's, you hear a hissing sound. "Pssssttt, over here." A shady figure beckons you. He or she is dressed for an Arctic winter.

"You must have got my message. What is my favourite fruit then?" the figure asks mysteriously.

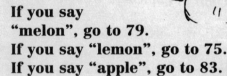

If you say "melon", go to 79.
If you say "lemon", go to 75.
If you say "apple", go to 83.

68 As the fête gets going, you see very few of your classmates around. A couple of them have already moved out of the valley with their families. But most people have stayed away from the fête because the stalls which are the most fun are missing. There's no apple bobbing stand, or water pistol shooting gallery because of the poisoned water.

No one rushes over to the books stall so you watch the people wandering around. You spot a few schoolkids forming a circle around Ms Sharp and some of the other teachers. They all seem to be complaining. You strain to hear what they're all saying. "Miss, Miss, where's the sponge throwing?" "We want the sponge throwing."

"Sponge throwing, sponge throwing!" all the children start to chant.

"Enough!" shouts Mr Grim.

"We can't have throwing wet sponges at the teachers, not with all that dangerous pollution in the water," explains Ms Sharp.

"Oh, go on…" pipes up one voice.

"It'll be even more fun. I'd pay double," chips in another voice."

"Silence!" roars Mr Grim.

Go to 112.

69 You come across two stout wooden doors straight ahead. One is labelled The Darkroom, the other is labelled The Inner Sanctum. Which one do you open?

If you choose The Darkroom, go to 166.
If you choose The Inner Sanctum, go to 137.

70

.rood xelpmoc cixoT eht ot
edoc eht lauqe oediv eht no
sesicrexe ehT

Go to 22.

71 You open the wooden chest and find a whole series of strange costumes. Some look familiar. Of course! They are the costumes of Biceps Man and his enemies! Teddy Toxic really does like Biceps Man! You pick up an enormous head mask and rack your brains for the character. It's the fiendish Drakor Thumb-Twister.

If you want to hold on to the mask, add it to your list.
Go to 140.

72 "Oh the 'Never Mind The Toxic' ones, I know the pair you mean, uh, I, like, wore them on my, uh, brilliant comeback tour. They are, uh, a little, like, uh, dirty," says Toxic.

"That's okay, they're the ones I'm after," you whoop excitedly.

"OK, send me, like, some proof that you have issue 219 and I'll be in touch," Toxic rings off abruptly.

You pull out the middle pages of the *Biceps Man* comic and send them to Toxic. Now all you have to do is wait.

If you have a school trip note, go to 32.
If not, go to 16.

73 You tiptoe through the building trying not to disturb any alarms. You reach a large area with an open door on the other side. You start to walk over to the door when you freeze with your foot a centimetre above the first carpet tile. This must be the amazing electrified carpet that the guide was talking about.

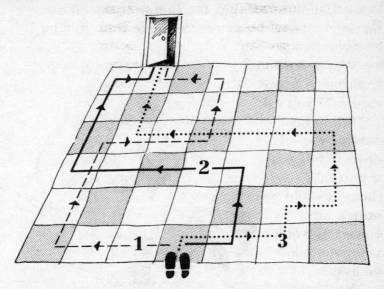

You stare at the black and white carpet tiles ahead. You know that many have been rigged with alarms, which detect footsteps. You try to think of a way across without setting off an alarm.

If you think it's route one, go to 118.
If you think it's route two, go to 99.
If you think it's route three, go to 59.

74 You run into the main part of the village. You can feel the glare of the jeep's many headlights. Toxic is catching up.

If you still have the envelope with you, go to 191.
If you don't have the envelope, go to 176.

75 "Good, good," says the figure, unbuttoning the overcoat and taking off the hat. It's Doug 'Deadline' Dennis, the Editor of the *Eldon Gazette*. "Phew! I was sweltering in that little lot," he says.

"Why were you wearing so many clothes?" you ask.

"Got to be careful, especially now. To tell you the truth, I thought you'd be here a lot earlier. Haven't you got a bike?" he asks.

"No, I was hoping for a mountain bike for my birthday but all I got was two stupid Biceps Man comics."

"Oh, bad luck, I guess it's the cost of all this bottled water, eh?"

You nod.

"I called you here because I spotted you at the library asking about Teddy Toxic. A good journalist always follows his leads," he says proudly. "Well, here's all I have on Mr Toxic. It's not much," he says, handing you a thin file.

"Don't look at it now. I've only got time to explain a few things quickly." Doug Dennis continues talking while turning his head this way and that. He seems very nervous.

"Teddy Toxic is to blame for Eldon's fizzy water. He's doing it so that people will accept his cut price offers for their houses. Then he can buy up the whole valley for next to nothing."

"Wow! That's just like the story in the comic," you think.

"He wants to turn the valley into the country's biggest car park."

"How do you know this?"

"It's a long story and I haven't got time to explain now," says Doug Dennis, glancing around anxiously. "All I will tell you is that the paper's photographer, Steve Griffiths, was on an assignment when he caught Teddy Toxic tipping huge barrels of chemicals into the reservoir at the top of the valley.

"Steve only took one photo before being chased off by two huge fierce dogs. He's in hiding somewhere, too afraid to come back to Eldon. He sent me a letter, the photo and a floppy disk with some code on it. The photo shows Teddy Toxic wearing a pair of his famous wild trousers and tipping chemicals into the reservoir."

"But that must be enough evidence to prove that he's guilty?"

"Yes, if I still had it, but my offices were ransacked yesterday. A short note was left made of letters cut out of newspapers. It suggested that I leave Eldon quickly."

"What are you going to do?"

"Precisely what the letter says."

You start to protest, but Doug Dennis interrupts. He's getting even more edgy.

Add the Toxic file to your list and then go to 8.

76 The screen fades back to black.
"Can I see that again?" you ask.

"No, the spirits have spoken," Mystic Mary says. "Now, go."

"But please."

"Go."

"At least tell me who you are?"

"I thought you would have guessed from the way I look at the stars," the fortune teller says. "Now hop it!"

You stumble out of the tent into the bright daylight. Your mind's racing from your visit to Mystic Mary. You're just in time for the obstacle race.

Go to 135.

77 "S... so... sor... sorry, Sir," bleats Mr Hapless, trembling in front of an angry-looking Teddy Toxic. Toxic has marched you back to the school group and ordered the guide to escort

the other children back on to the school minibus.
The trip to the ToxCo Complex is over.

"As I've already said, Mr Toxic, I am most
dreadfully sorry," bleats Mr Hapless. "There will be
a full written apology to you and I can assure you
that this child will be punished in the strongest
possible way."

"Yeah, yeah, yeah. OK, just, uh, make sure, like
none of your meddling children, ever come near
my offices again, you hear?"

"Yes, Mr Toxic. Sorry about that."

You daren't say a word.

If you have the photo, go to 154.
If you haven't got the photo, go to 97.

78 Although the track looks shorter, it winds
back and forth. You head over a slight rise
in the track only to find both vehicles blocking the
road ahead. You can see Teddy Toxic and Mr
Hapless at the wheels of their vehicles. Both look
very angry indeed...

Go to 109.

79 "Melon? Melon!" the figure hisses. "If
you're not good enough at decoding simple
messages, then there's no point listening to what
I've got to say." With that, the figure turns and
walks briskly away, stopping only once to shout,
"Don't follow me."

Go to 12.

80 You start to flick through the Biceps Man comics but soon tire of the lame stories and the pathetic hero.

Miss Jenkins quickly prices each *Biceps Man* comic at 50p each. You have 90p and can afford to buy one of them. Do you want to use up most of your money on one comic?

If you want to buy a comic, write down which issue you choose and go to 94.
If you want to save your money, go to 11.

81 Picking up a large padded envelope from the bedside table, you cram the trousers and the photo inside. Your heart's pounding with excitement.

"If I can get these to the police, I've done it. Toxic will be history," you declare to the empty Inner Sanctum. Unfortunately, it isn't empty any more.

"History, oh I don't think so," leers Teddy Toxic. Two enormous dogs, one on each side of him, growl and bear their enormous teeth. You break out into a sweat.

If you have the Drakor Thumb-Twister mask, go to 113.
If not, go to 196.

82 You open the slightly torn envelope and read the message inside. It seems to be in some sort of code. Can you work it out?

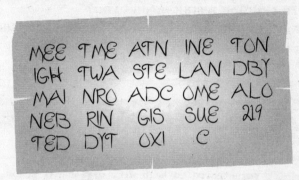

Try to work out what the code says and then go to 110.

83 "You didn't get my message, did you?" the figure curses.

"Yes I did, honest," you protest, but it's too late. The shady character stomps off in a huff. You try to follow, but you're too slow and the figure disappears almost immediately.

Go to 12.

84 When you get home, your mum's on the telephone. You hear her chatting away to a neighbour. "Really, the Woodwards and the Patels are moving too? What a shame." The Patels – that's Satinda's family. You know you must solve the crisis quickly.

"Can I go out tonight?" you ask.

"No, you've got your schoolwork to do," replies Jim.

"What about tomorrow?"

"No, it's the school fête."

"But it doesn't start until the afternoon."

"Not for me and your mother, perhaps, but you're running a stall, aren't you?"

"No, I'm not. After last year, I made sure that I didn't volunteer again."

⭐ ELDON SCHOOL

Your child has kindly and generously volunteered to help with our annual school fête on Saturday.

Your child has asked to work on the ....BOOK...... stall and will be looked after by our English teacher, Miss Jenkins.

Your child will be needed from 10am to 4pm. School uniform is compulsory for all our helpers.

Thank you

Mr C Sharp

Ms Sharp
Headmistress

"Oh, I think you did," says Jim sternly. He pulls out a letter from a drawer and hands it to you. You groan. Not the boring book stall again. You had a nightmare time last year with your deadly dull English teacher, Miss Jenkins, and you've been lumbered with her and her silly stall again.

"You can't go making promises and then letting people down, you know," Jim says. You nod gloomily in agreement.

Go to 29.

85 Go to 103.

86 Mrs Patel shows you the second picture.

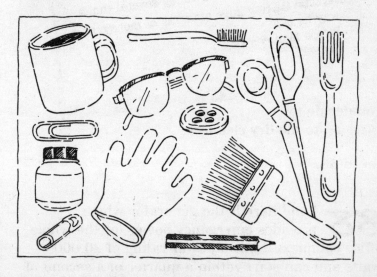

Count to 20 and immediately go to 27.

87

Name: Theodore Joseph Lesley Tocsolivas

Address: ToxCo Complex, Eldon Valley but believed to have other houses around the country.

Age: Unknown (Between 40-45)

Family: Unknown

Distinguishing features: Two gold teeth. Safety-pin earring. Usually wears very bright, patterned trousers.

Background: Found some fame in the late 1970s with the Punk band, Teddy Toxic and His Toxettes. Biggest hit – 'Fast Car Fury' which reached No.16 in the charts. Band broke up in 1981.

His one comeback attempt ended in complete disaster. Disappeared for many years, possible criminal connections, before reappearing as head of mysterious ToxCo company. Has tried to buy Eldon Valley several times.

Interests: Making huge amounts of money, any way he can.
Biceps Man comics.
Himself.

You decide to carry on to the dry cleaners.

Go to 58.

88 "And here is the generator which provides emergency power for the whole office complex. It has a power rating of 20,000 watts and can start within a quarter of a second of a power cut…" There's no doubt about it. The guide showing you around the ToxCo complex is the most boring person in the entire world.

"This way to the computing offices," says the guide, punching buttons on a codepad. A door slides open.

"I hope you don't have copies of that awful Toxman computer game here," says Mr Hapless sternly.

"Oh, no, no, of course not," says the guide blushing a little. "I know, let's take a look at the workshops instead." The guide leads you all a different way and presses a triangle-shaped button three times. An electric door hisses open and the guide leads you along a stone-floored corridor.

Go to 138.

89 You throw the big envelope into the hedge and continue running. You can feel the beam of the jeep's headlights burning your head and shoulders. You dodge down a small alleyway and out on to the road near the village green. Looking back, you see that the jeep has stopped chasing you.

You look down and see Teddy Toxic's jeep parked where you were standing a moment ago.

"He must be searching for the envelope," you think.

You suddenly hear an enormous shout and the sound of the jeep's engine starting up again. At that moment you also spot a furious Mr Hapless walking towards you. Gulp!

Go to 129.

90 Tired and bruised from all the poor vaults you make and the inevitable 50 press-ups from Mr Grim for doing them badly, you limp home from school. On the way back, you wander past two more 'For Sale' signs. Everyone's moving. You've got to reveal Teddy Toxic's evil plan quickly.

Go to 21.

91 You trip over one of the cardboard boxes and a number of old records spill out on to the floor. You see they're all the same, a checked cover with *'Never Mind The Toxic'* written on them. As you go to put them back into their box, a photo slips out of one of them.

That's it. That's the photo of Teddy Toxic tipping toxic waste into the Eldon Valley reservoir. You hurry out of the Darkroom, switching off its red light as you leave.

Add the photo to your list and go to 182.

92 As Toxic scampers off crying, you rush in the opposite direction. You reach the police station in no time and spot friendly PC Coppit on the front desk.

"I need to see the Inspector quickly," you puff breathlessly, "I have vital new evidence about the water problem," you gasp, slapping the trousers on to the desk in front of you.

"A pair of trousers? Hardly stunning evidence, is it?" says PC Coppit, frowning.

If you have the photo, go to 116.
If not, go to 192.

93 You start down the track but the vehicles seem to be gaining. Your path takes you across the road. As you reach the road, you can see the speeding school minibus getting closer. Amazingly, it's still ahead of Teddy Toxic's jeep but not for long. As you cross the road, Teddy Toxic speeds past the minibus and throws drawing pins on to the road. The school minibus blows a tyre.

You grit your teeth with fear as the minibus skids left, then right. You pray that it will be all right.

Go to 171.

94 You tuck the comic into your bag underneath the stall's tables and throw 50p into the money tin.

Write 40p in your money box and go to 11.

95 Back in the outer part of the complex, in front of the security carpet tiles, the ToxCo guide is giving Mr Hapless a real telling off.

"Your supposedly 'lost' schoolchild has broken into Mr Toxic's personal quarters, you idiot!"

"Hang on a minute…"

"There's no doubt about it. We can't follow the hooligan, we'll just have to wait. I'll notify Mr Toxic."

"But I thought Mr Toxic wasn't here?" says Mr Hapless puzzled.

"I don't have to tell stupid schoolteachers the whole truth," the guide snaps, picking up a telephone.

Go to 81.

96 Back at the wasteland, Teddy Toxic has examined the comic carefully and has a satisfied smirk written all over his ugly face.

"Just, uh, one more thing, then you can, like, go, kid." Toxic smirks. "I'll have those, uh, trousers back, or I'll set Rock and Roll on to you and it won't be, uh, pretty."

"But it's a fair trade," you protest, shivering as you glance at the dogs.

"It would be fair if you were, like, really interested in Punk Rock but you've been, uh,

snooping around a lot and, like, my sources tell me that you're more interested in pinning the blame on me, uh, for tampering with the water," Toxic replies.

"Well, it was you who poisoned the water, wasn't it?" you say.

"Why of course it was," Toxic laughs. "But, uh, I don't intend to be blamed for anything. You don't think, uh, that I'm going to let you have, like, the trousers with fizzy chemicals spilt all over them, do you? Now, uh, hand them over," growls Toxic, loosening his grip on the leads holding his ferocious hounds.

With no way of escaping those dogs, you have no choice but to limply hand the trousers back to Toxic. As he turns to leave, he gives the most enormous yelp of fear.

Go to 187.

97 You're stuck in the detention room and stuck on this ridiculously hard maths problem. On the other side of the room, Mr Hapless sits reading an enormous computer manual.

"Sir. I've been here for ages. When can I leave?" you plead.

"When you've completed that maths problem."

"But it could take all night," you complain.

"Don't worry. I've arranged with your mum and stepdad for you to stay here as long as it takes," he smiles wickedly. He points to sleeping bags, a tray of sandwiches and a huge shiny flask.

"You should think yourself lucky to be locked up here. Your stepdad looked furious when we told him what you'd been up to."

You've well and truly failed. Eldon Valley will be sold and everyone you know will have to move out. Evil Teddy Toxic has a lot to answer for!

THE END

---

98 "With the great help of the students from the Swallowtown Drama School, I declare the Eldon School Fête open," the mayoress says. She snips a piece of blue ribbon between the wrought iron school gates. A few people clap and then wander through the gates.

You suddenly realize that the Eco Warriors attend the drama school in Swallowtown! Your heart races, but you can't see any of them.

Mr Grim, your dreaded P.E. teacher, looks even more serious than usual. So does your headmistress, Ms Sharp. Last year, there was a huge crowd waiting to get in. This time, only a

couple of dozen people, mainly adults, drift
through the school gates.

"Oh, I'm sure it will pick up," says Miss Jenkins,
all smiles. Ms Sharp and Mr Grim glare at her. You
stifle a giggle. Everyone knows that Miss Jenkins
lives in her own little world of books. It's not fair,
kids get told off for dreaming.

Go to 68.

99 You step on a corner tile. "Wrong route,"
blares a metallic voice. From hidden
speakers in the ceiling comes the sound of some
very, very bad music. The volume rises until it's
almost deafening. It seems that you have only two
choices, both very risky. You can carry on into
Toxic's offices or race back to rejoin the group,
hopefully before anyone spots that you are missing.

Do you head into Toxic's quarters (go to 53)?
Do you head back (go to 173)?

100 The screen asks for a player code. If unsure, the screen prompt says, type in the numbers 008.

If you have the tips card from Rob and want to look at it, go to 132.
If not, choose a code to enter and then go to 172.

101 You continue along the corridor and past the ladder. You quickly glance at the clock and make a vital mistake. Crash! Toxman falls into an Ecotrap.

Go to 177.

102 She shows you the first picture.

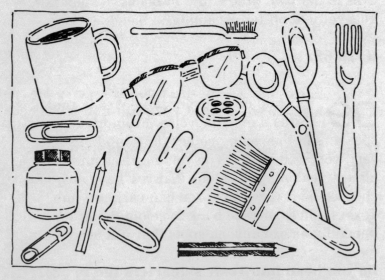

Count to 20 and immediately turn to 86.

103 "Wrong code" sounds a metallic voic Suddenly, a really loud hooter starts hooting and the sound of some dreadful Punk Rock music echoes through the whole building. You stand stock still, trying to decide what to do. You suddenly feel hot breath on your neck...

Go to 164.

104 Satisfied that the competition is well and truly beaten, Mr Grim turns and heads for the line at full speed. He doesn't see the banana skin ahead and, stepping on it, does the smartest and fastest backwards somersault you've ever seen. The people watching the race laugh and clap.

Go to 146.

105 To pass the time, you decide to look through one of the magazines on the stall.

If you choose the *Biceps Man* comics, go to 80.
If you choose a *Poptastic!* 1978 annual, go to 25.
If you choose an old puzzle magazine, go to 120.

106 "Wrong, I'm afraid," announces Mrs Patel. You say goodbye and leave the memory game stall.

Go to 135.

107 As soon as you start along your chosen track, you realize that it's longer than you thought. In the distance you can hear the roar of engines. What are you going to do?
If you want to cut across to track 1, go to 93.
If you want to cut across to track 4, go to 124.
If you want to continue along this track, go to 78.

108 Several months later and long after all the trouble you were in has been forgotten, you're beginning to settle into your new home. The place is not as nice as your old house but it was all Swallowtown Council could provide so quickly.

The new school is not too bad, but some of the teachers make Mr Grim, your scary old P.E. teacher, seem friendly in comparison. But what you miss most about Eldon is your friends and the lovely pretty valley.

If you visited Inspector Marchbank earlier in the adventure, go to 179.
If not, go to 194.

109 "What do you think you are doing?" roars Mr Hapless. His normal, friendly nature has evaporated. Teddy Toxic advances and grabs the envelope containing the photo and the trousers.
"I'll take those, kid," he snarls, clipping you around the ear.

Mr Hapless turns to Teddy Toxic. "Dreadfully sorry, Mr Toxic. I don't know what to say."

"How about, nothing, teach. I've got my uh, trousers back, so I'm, uh, like, going." Toxic stomps off to his jeep and in a cloud of dust wheelspins the gleaming white vehicle away.

"You're really for it!" screams Sandra Lockwood delightedly out of the minibus window. With the photo and the trousers gone, and with Mr Hapless looking as if he's about to explode, you have to agree with her.

Go to 129

110

The message reads:

Meet me at nine, tonight wasteland by main road Come alone. Bring issue 219. Teddy Toxic

Go to 197.

111

ANSWERS

1 CAT, ANT, CRAB, TIGER, ELEPHANT, LION, HORSE, WALRUS, FOX, BEAR

2 YES

3 GEOGRAPHY, MATHEMATICS, HISTORY

Go to 114.

112 You smile and watch the kids slowly drifting off to the various attractions.

"Remember the teachers' and parents' obstacle race is at 3 o'clock," blares Mr Hapless's voice over the school tannoy.

"Huh, it's not going to be as much fun as usual without the water obstacles," you say out loud.

"What was that, dear?" Miss Jenkins overhears.

"Oh nothing," you reply, scattering the few naff romantic novels and tatty, ancient schoolbooks you have around, to try to make them fill the big wooden tables of your stall. Someone in a gorilla outfit wanders up to the stall.

"No books on monkeys I'm afraid," you joke. The gorilla says nothing. It just leafs through a few of the books in an uninterested sort of way. When Miss Jenkins' back is turned it quickly pulls out a small bundle of *Biceps Man* comics from inside its suit.

"Some of these are very old. They should make good bait…" says the gorilla, But before you can comment, the gorilla has gone.

Do you ask Miss Jenkins if she saw the gorilla (go to 7) or do you keep quiet (go to 49)?

113 You point the mask at Teddy Toxic defensively.

"Oh my, uh, silly old Drakor mask. That cost me a fortune to, like, have built. It's perfect in every way, uh, I mean, it's, like, perfect, except it has no, uh, laser bolts, uh, of course." Suddenly, Toxic doesn't seem quite so cocky.

You fumble with the mask trying to find a trigger

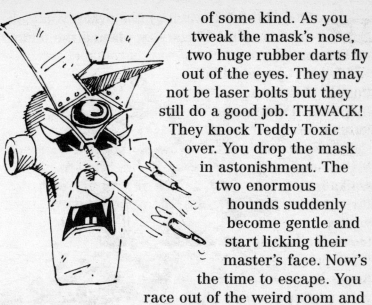

of some kind. As you tweak the mask's nose, two huge rubber darts fly out of the eyes. They may not be laser bolts but they still do a good job. THWACK! They knock Teddy Toxic over. You drop the mask in astonishment. The two enormous hounds suddenly become gentle and start licking their master's face. Now's the time to escape. You race out of the weird room and back into the Toxco complex. As you escape, you dash past your classmates. All you hear is an astonished "What the…?" from Mr Hapless and a "Grab that kid!" from the ToxCo guide.

Remove the mask from your list and go to 66.

114 Do you want to look at another book (go to 105) or not (go to 11)?

115 The game starts. You've got 50 seconds to reach the big sludge release button at the top of the screen. You see a platform ahead and a ladder to one side.

If you take the ladder go to 160.
If you go straight ahead go to 101.

116 "Oh, I think you'll find it is, when you look at this picture," you say, placing the photo on the counter.

"Crikey!" exclaims PC Coppit. "Inspector, Inspector! Come and look at this."

Inspector Marchbank walks into the room with a frown. PC Coppit hands  your evidence to her. She immediately barks orders into her radio, "All units. All units. Arrest Teddy Toxic, repeat, Teddy Toxic." She turns to PC Coppit. "Make sure we have a dog handler with the arresting officers to look after Toxic's ghastly hounds."

"Yes, ma'am," Coppit replies, disappearing into a back office.

Go to 153.

---

117 Toxic flicks through the three magazines. "My sources told me that issue 219 might be here."

"Sorry, it was sold earlier," you smugly reply.

"What! But I must uh, like, have it to complete my collection. I need Biceps Man fighting the Shopping Trolley of Hell, I want, I want, I want!"

he starts a tantrum but controls himself when he sees Miss Jenkins staring at him.

"Do you remember who bought it?" You're caught in the uncomfortable stare of Teddy Toxic's angry eyes.

You feel very scared but stand fast.

"N...N...No, I can't remember," you reply but don't sound as convincing as you would have liked.

Toxic grabs you by your school shirt. "Liar!" he screams. "Tell me who bought it! If I want something, I must have it, I will have it!" he screams, shaking you up and down.

"Mr Toxic, STOP THAT!" Miss Jenkins shrill shriek cuts through the air.

"I want that magazine, so if you remember who has it, put them into contact wih me immediately. Here's a donation to your pathetic little fête," hisses Toxic, tossing a wad of five pound notes on to the stall table before stomping off.

"What a dreadful man!" exclaims Miss Jenkins. You're shaken, but inside you are really excited. Perhaps the Biceps Man comic you just bought will help you foil Teddy Toxic's evil plan.

Go to 22.

118 Go to 99.

119 Back from the school trip, there's a half-opened letter for you.

Go to 82.

120

1 Find the names of 10 creatures in this word block

A	T	B	A	C	A	T	R
T	N	A	H	P	E	L	E
B	A	R	S	L	N	O	G
U	G	C	N	H	A	I	I
B	O	L	I	O	N	A	T
E	W	A	L	R	U	S	O
X	O	F	E	S	M	Y	R
H	C	R	A	E	B	I	G

2 Sammy the seal is doing two of his favourite tricks. Is he using the same pole in both?

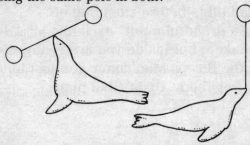

3 Name these 3 jumbled-up school subjects:

HYGPAOGER   **THMETAMISCA**   **YSRHTIO**

If you want to try any of the puzzles or quiz questions, you can turn to 111 to spot the answers afterwards.
If not, go to 114.

121 Down the ladder Toxman goes. Another platform appears. Ahead is another ladder. There's no choice but to take the ladder going up. You glance at the clock on the screen. You've used 25 seconds already.

Go to 131.

122 The Eldon Gazette offices are closed and locked. You rattle the door but it's no use. Turning round, you spot the gleaming white jeep between you and the police station. What are you going to do?

Do you run into the village (go to 74)?
Do you want to hide the package in a nearby hedge (go to 89)?
Do you want to post the package in the post box (go to 195)?

123 The guide's tour and lecture doesn't get any more interesting. It takes all of your strength just to stay awake.

Go to 161.

124 You head down the track but are quickly outpaced by the two vehicles speeding along the road. Just as your path crosses the road, both the jeep and the school minibus screech to a halt in front of you, blocking your way.

Go to 109.

125 You enter a tent, misty with burning incense sticks. "Sit down child and I will tell you the secrets you want to hear." Normally, Mystic Mary is played by your stuttering Biology teacher, Mr Webb, but this fortune teller looks completely different.

Behind her veil, Mystic Mary's eyes start fluttering up and down. Her whole body starts swaying, first to the left and then to the right. "Concentrate on the magical screen in front of you and it will reveal untold wonders," she says. You are not convinced. Still, watching an unknown adult making such a fool of themselves is well worth the money.

Cross off the money from your list and go straight to 130.

126 Toxman eventually gets up. You can only move him to the right.

Go to 163.

127 "Hurry up and sort out your room," shouts your mum from downstairs. It sounds a little like most Saturday mornings. Sadly, she doesn't mean just tidy it up. That's already been done. In fact, your room has never looked tidier. All your music tapes and computer games are packed in strong cardboard boxes. Your clothes have already disappeared downstairs, carried by Jim in a battered brown suitcase.

It's a couple of weeks since you failed to get the evidence to the police that would have convinced them of Teddy Toxic's guilt. Your family have accepted Toxic's offer on your house and today is moving out day.

"There's someone on the phone for you," shouts your mum.

"Probably a friend," mutters your stepdad packing mum's best china into a wooden tea chest.

You walk past him carefully, trudge down the stairs and pick up the phone.

"Hello, it's Doug Dennis here. I received an interesting package yesterday morning..." he pauses for effect.

"Yes, go on," you say impatiently.

"...containing a photo and a pair of patterned trousers."

"But how? I don't understand."

"I assumed you posted it, but forgot to put an address on," says Doug Dennis. "Fortunately, a contact of mine at the Swallowtown Sorting Office checks unaddressed letters and when he saw the trousers, he sent the parcel straight to me."

"B-b-b-b-but... so?" you stutter.

"So," laughs Doug, "I handed it over to the

police who've let the scientists analyse the chemicals on the trousers. Now they know exactly what they are, they believe that they can sort out Eldon's water in a week or two."

"And Teddy Toxic...?"

"Already arrested and likely to be behind bars for a long, long time."

"You're a hero! Hello, are you still there... hello?" But you've dropped the phone and to the astonishment of your mum, you're dancing around the hallway. "I've saved Eldon, I've saved Eldon!" you cry bouncing around.

Shocked, your mum picks up the phone and puts it to her ear. At about the same time, you bump into Jim. After a wobble one way and then the other, he drops the tea chest full of china on to the floor. There's a horrible smashing sound followed by an icy silence as Jim glares at you and then turns with a really worried frown to your mum. After all, it was her best china.

But your mum doesn't seem bothered about it at all. In fact, for the first time in weeks, she's got a broad smile on her face.

"Well, thank you very much for the news, Mr Dennis," she says and puts the phone down. She looks at both of you and then does something extraordinary. She pulls a silly face, dissolves into an enormous fit of giggles and then starts dancing round the hall with you!

When your mum's giggles eventually stop, she turns to your stepdad.

"Don't worry about the breakages, Jim. I think our kid here can afford to pay!" she says.

"What?" you stare aghast.

"Well, you have got £10,000 of reward money to spend! Now, Jim, be a love and unpack the car. We're staying in Eldon for good."

Hooray!

THE END

---

128 With a mechanical hiss, the door slides smoothly open. You tiptoe through it and keep low to avoid the security cameras swivelling this way and that. They're designed for adult intruders, not someone of your height, so you can easily creep beneath them.

Go to 73.

129 The next day, after huge tellings-off from just about every teacher at school, you retrace your journey down through the village to try and recover the evidence, but it's no use. It looks like Teddy Toxic is now completely safe from the police and that his plan of buying up Eldon will succeed.

Not only have you failed to save Eldon, you've also got four weeks of two hour-long detentions to look forward to. Your mum and stepdad are furious too. You feel really miserable.

If you put the package in the postbox, go to 127. If not, go to 108.

130 The screen does indeed come to life. At first you're very disappointed – it's just a camcorder viewer. But as you watch, you realize that it could reveal very important information.

Go to 76.

131 At the top of the ladder, there are platforms going both to the left and to the right.

Do you send Toxman right (go to 156)?
Do you send Toxman left (go to 145)?

132

FREE WITH GAMER MAGAZINE

TOXMAN TIPS CARD

🪜 = LADDERS UP + DOWN `SAFE`

⛰ = ECOTRAPS `AVOID`

▭ = PLATFORM `SAFE`

▬ = PLATFORM CRUMBLES `AVOID`
[safe if you have power pill]

✹ = POWER PILL `GRAB!`

Some early/review copies allow you to start on final screen by typing 504

Go to 100.

133 What bad timing! If you'd been just one minute later, Teddy Toxic and his two ferocious dogs wouldn't have been wandering through the Inner Sanctum room. Unfortunately, as you open the door, you see them. It's obvious that they are not happy to see you...

Go to 196.

134 Before you start the game, you check on your stepdad. He's still fiddling with his bonfire at the far end of the garden. You've got plenty of time.

Go to 100.

135 "The teachers and parents obstacle race will start in two minutes." The voice of Mr Hapless booms over the school tannoy. Silly Mr Hapless leaves the microphone switched on so that everyone can hear him whisper to himself under his breath, "that just about gives me time to get my trainers on. Though I don't know why I'm entering. That awful yob, Mr Grim, wins every time."

Mr Hapless's gaff brings smiles to many of the people at the fête. You decide to watch the race, and wander over to your friend, Rob. He's standing near the finish line. "Finished your chores, bookworm?" he jokes.

Go to 5.

136 As you guide Toxman down the ladder, you spot the time display on the screen. It says 003. Just three seconds to reach the end of the game. You drop the joystick on to the table and put your head in your hands. You've failed.

Go to 177.

137 Go to 133.

138 As the guide leads you towards the workshops, Mr Hapless asks about the security measures in the complex.

"Oh it's all automated. We've got security cameras and an amazing alarm system under the carpet tiles near Mr Toxic's personal offices. I'd love to show you, but Mr Toxic expressly forbids anyone to go near the area."

"No security guards?" asks Mr Hapless.

"No," answers the guide. "Mr Toxic likes as few people here as possible. It's only because he's away on business that he's allowed a school trip here."

The class, led by the chattering guide and Mr Hapless, enter the workshops. Some of the other pupils gasp at several of the homemade posters on the wall. The guide spots the children's glances and, quick as a flash, stands in front of them.

Mr Hapless doesn't notice. He's all excited about some piece of electronics or other.

"Isn't that a 32-bit register flange assembly valve?" your silly maths teacher enthuses.

"Why, yes, I believe it is," answers the guide, tearing down the two posters and throwing them into a bin. The guide starts lecturing the class about various pieces of computer software and hardware. His talk is even more boring than before.

If you've planned a trade with Teddy Toxic, go to 123. If not, go to 43.

139 Toxman runs along the platform which suddenly starts crumbling. You move Toxman as fast as you can.

Just as you see the safety of a ladder ahead, the platform beneath Toxman's three feet falls away. Down tumbles Toxman straight into an Ecotrap. Blast!

Go to 177.

140 **Do you want to look in the wooden chest (go to 71)?**
Do you pull the rope (go to 169)?
Do you head for the other door (go to 175)?

141 Tiptoeing into Teddy Toxic's private offices, you're amazed to find all the doors wide open. Teddy Toxic must be very relaxed indeed.

If you have the photo, go to 182.
If not, go to 69.

142 You play the sports video tape. The tape features top workout instructor Ivor Calfstrain in his studio with a few celebrities, not that you recognise any of them. You quickly bore of all the moves, first demonstrated by Ivor then copied badly by his overweight and unfit guests.

Hang on, there's something wrong with the video. It seems to freeze frame by mistake. After three of these freeze frames, the tape stops.

You run the tape backwards carefully watching the freeze frames. Just as you get to the third, a horrible clunking sound indicates all is not well with the tape.

You pull the cassette out of the video recorder watching metre upon metre of tape spool out. Oh dear, that's ruined it. But what were those freeze framed pictures all about?

Go to 61.

143 No, no, NO! Toxman has fallen through a gap in the platform and landed in an Ecotrap.

Go to 177.

144 "I don't have a pair like those," Toxic says, "are you sure you know what you're talking about?"

"Y...y...yes," you stutter.

"No, you don't. I don't like people mucking me around," Toxic slams the phone down. There's no way he is going to trade trousers with you now.

Go to 48.

145 A choice of directions greets you on screen. There's a ladder going up or a corridor running along. Which way do you guide Toxman?

Should Toxman go up the ladder (go to 168)? Should Toxman go along the corridor (go to 148)?

146 With Mr Grim still on the ground, your stepdad runs past and breaks the winning tape. Everyone cheers loudly. Mr Grim manages to get up and hobbles in after your stepdad, Mr Lockwood and Satinda's dad, Kumar.

A full ten minutes pass before the very last competitor, Mr Hapless of course, struggles to the line, still with the potato sack wrapped around one foot. By that time the village doctor, Doctor McKenzie, is bandaging up Mr Grim's swollen ankle. Mr Grim is moaning and groaning.

"It's only a sprain. Honestly Grim, you're worse than a schoolchild," snaps the doctor. Everyone who hears the comment grins. Eventually, your stepdad goes over to the mayoress to receive his prize.

"Ahem," coughs the mayoress, "Well, we all thought, er, Mr Grim would win, er, as he usually does... er... so the prize is a video on physical fitness."

"Thank you very much," says your stepdad, at first a little disappointed. He cheers up as he accepts the prize and holds it aloft to hearty cheers from the small crowd.

You look around for the gorilla but it seems to have disappeared along with Godzilla and Mystic Mary. How strange.

"Come on Superman," jokes your mum, leading your stepdad away from people shaking his hand or patting his back. "It's only a school obstacle race."

"Yeah, but it's the first bit of luck we've had in ages," Jim replies. "Even if the prize was a silly sports video."

Smiling, you all walk home. It's certainly been the most eventful school fête that you can remember and some of the things that happened may even help you to defeat Teddy Toxic.

"Here you go. Maybe you'll be able to swap this at school for something," says Jim, handing you the video.

Add the sports video to your list and go to 19.

147 You try to play the game again, but the screen says, "Demo version - 2 plays only."

Go to 61.

148 Whoops! Down falls Toxman into an Ecotrap.

Go to 177.

149 As you walk home from school, you pass by an alleyway near the village bakery and hear a sound.

"Pssst, over here." Oh, here we go again, you think.

"I haven't got much time," Stargazer says. "I

should already be back at college, being told off with the others. I just wanted to catch you and check that you got all of our clues, the video and everything. Good luck."

"You mean you're not going to help me any more?" you say dismayed.

"Afraid not. I've got to go."

You trudge back home thinking about the trip to the ToxCo complex tomorrow.

Go to 88.

150 Down the ladder Toxman races, his three legs a blur of action. The platform extends both left and right. Which way should he go?

If you choose left, go to 186.
If you choose right, go to 143.

151 Coming home late from school after completing a detention, your mum meets you at the door.

"There's a letter for you, dear, it looks a bit battered," she says.

Go to 82.

152 Toxman can now only go left. You guide him along the platform.

Go to 145.

153 You explain all about the chemicals on the trousers. The Inspector heartily congratulates you. Just as you're leaving the station, another policeman walks in with two familiar faces. It's Stargazer and Earthwatcher – the Eco Warriors! "I found these two students dancing on the village green dressed in this stupid fancy dress. I think they're drunk, Madam," the policeman says, as Inspector Marchbank frowns.

"We're not drunk, we're just very, very happy," laughs Stargazer.

"We're superheroes, you know," jokes Earthwatcher.

"One superhero, to be exact," corrects Stargazer.

"They sound drunk," Inspector Marchbank agrees with the other policeman.

"They're certainly not," you shout. "These two have helped save Eldon as much as I have!"

Inspector Marchbank looks at you in surprise. You start to explain all about Biceps Man.

Go to 167.

154 When you eventually get the chance, you go and see Inspector Marchbank and show her the photo. "Hurumph!" she scowls. "So you and your Eco Warrior friends are now faking photographs to frame Teddy Toxic. He's most definitely innocent you know. Now get out of this police station immediately before I arrest you for obstructing police justice."

Go to 193.

155 "Another game?" the screen asks.

If you want to try again, go to 172.
If not, go to 45.

156 You see a power pill ahead. You guide Toxman over it. PING! The speaker crackles into life with the sound of a short burst of applause.

Add the power pill to your list and go to 152.

157 Just as you make your decision to stay, the guide receives a message on his electronic beeper.

"I'm afraid Mr Toxic says he wants you all to leave."

"But why?" asks Mr Hapless.

"He doesn't say," the guide answers back.

Some of the kids smile with relief but Mr Hapless looks crestfallen.

Rats! You had a chance to creep away and didn't take it. Trudging back to the school minibus, you think about the failed opportunity.

"Come on grumpy, the trip wasn't as bad as all that," grins horrible Sandra Lockwood.

"Push off, ugly," you snarl. If only she knew.

If you have the photo of Teddy Toxic at the reservoir, go to 154, otherwise, go to 193.

158 Out of the ToxCo complex you run. You leap over the fence and dash down the hill. Stopping for a brief moment, you turn round and spy Teddy Toxic climbing into his jeep while Mr Hapless herds the other kids into the minibus. Soon, they're going to be after you – you've got to run as quickly as you can.

You breathlessly start heading down the side of the valley towards Eldon Village. The side of the valley is criss-crossed with many different footpaths and tracks. "Which one is the shortest route?" you wonder. You stare hard at the valley in front of you. You haven't much time to make a decision.

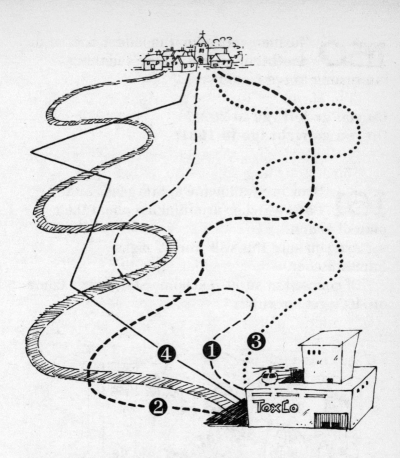

Allow yourself no more than 30 seconds to decide which track to pick.
If you choose track 1, go to 199.
If you choose track 2, go to 199.
If you choose track 3, go to 107.
If you choose track 4, go to 124.

159 "Invalid player code, replaced with 008," the screen says.

Go to 198.

160 Toxman climbs up the ladder and on to another platform. There's nothing interesting to see from here.

Do you go left (go to 202)?
Do you go right (go to 163)?

161 Over in Swallowtown, Stargazer and Earthwatcher are thinking about their plan of action.

"Are you sure this will work?" sighs Earthwatcher.

"Of course I'm sure!" exclaims Stargazer. "Come on, let's get on with it."

Soon they are hard at work in the costume room of their drama school.

"You realize that we'll definitely get expelled for this?" moans Earthwatcher.

"Oh shut up, John, and finish making those arms," says Stargazer, sculpting an ugly-looking giant face out of modelling clay. "So what if we get expelled? We're trying to save a whole village from extinction."

"You're right. We must help that brave kid," says Earthwatcher.

"And this disguise should help us," replies Stargazer adding, "How's your voice?"

"Oh, it'll be strong and loud enough," assures Earthwatcher.

If you've been on the school trip, go to 119, otherwise go to 151.

162 The noisy printer produces a printout which makes you gasp. It's the photo of Teddy Toxic that Doug Dennis described. It must have been stored on the end of the disk for security. You carefully put the printout in your pocket.

Add the photo to your list and go to 61.

163 Toxman runs along the corridor. Suddenly, a ladder appears going down.

Do you climb down the ladder (go to 121)?
Do you continue along the corridor (go to 148)?

164 You whirl around.
"What on earth do you think you're doing?" booms Mr Hapless. He's normally so quiet and friendly, it comes as quite a shock.

"S...s...sorry sir, just curious, I guess."

"You're standing next to me for the rest of the trip and when we get back to school, you can expect the biggest detention imaginable."

Rats! With Mr Hapless constantly watching you, there's no way you can escape and search the ToxCo complex. Defeated, you grumpily endure the rest of the afternoon's boring tour.

Go to 97.

165 You start the second screen by snapping up an oval-shaped power pill to give you the extra speed to run along a crumbling platform, but then disaster strikes. You fail to spot an Ecotrap, which Toxman falls into. A howl comes through the computer's tiny speakers.

Go to 177.

166 The Darkroom seems well named. Even when you switch on the dull red light, it's hard to see much through the gloom. You wander around, stumbling into furniture and boxes.

As your eyes get more accustomed to the poor light you can see large boxes and photos all over the place. Looking through lots of the photos, most seem to be either of a much younger and even uglier Teddy Toxic in his punk days or of offices and car parks.

"What a strange combination," you think.

Go to 91.

167 The next few days pass by in a whirl. Toxic is arrested and taken for trial in Swallowtown. The Police search the ToxCo Complex and find more evidence of his crimes.

For a very short time, you are the village hero. The mayoress declares a holiday for the village and at a small ceremony hands you a £20 pounds voucher for schoolbooks.

"What about the £10,000 reward money?" you ask. The mayoress grimaces awkwardly.

"Well, er, I'm afraid the reward was withdrawn before you solved the case."

After being a hero at school for a couple of days, the other kids quickly forget and soon life returns to normal. That means lots of schoolwork and vaulting practice with Mr Grim.

A couple of weeks later in assembly, you're caught whispering to Rob and sent to see the headmistress, Ms Sharp. "As you enter her office, you notice someone familiar standing next to her. It's Doug Dennis!

"Hello there, hero," he smiles. "I'm out of hiding at long last."

"Mr Dennis has fully explained your involvement and the efforts of the drama school pupils of Swallowtown," says Ms Sharp. "I'm going to ensure that the mayoress coughs up the reward money. This will allow the drama students to pay for their damage and continue their courses. I believe there may be enough money left to pay for a rather nice mountain bike. That was Mr Dennis's suggestion."

"Thank you, Doug."

"Oh, and tell your stepdad that I have a couple of Teddy Toxic records for him, if he ever dares play them!" laughs Doug Dennis.

THE END

168 Up on to a new platform Toxman races. He can go back and down the ladder or go forward. The screen shows the platform ahead. Part of it looks a little different.

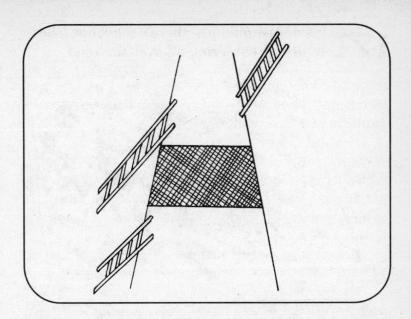

Do you want to go back and climb down the last ladder (go to 136)?
Do you want to continue forward (go to 170)?

169 You pull the rope and suddenly a large piece of the stone wall slides away revealing a clothes rail. Back in Teddy Toxic's bedroom, you almost faint with excitement. There, on the clothes rail, are the toxic trousers.

Add the toxic trousers to your list and go to 95.

170 If you have a power pill but want to save it, go to 201.
If you have a power pill and want to use it, go to 180.
If you don't have a power pill, go to 181.

171 Inside the minibus, there's mayhem. The vehicle is careering all over the road.

Most of the children are screaming but Mr Hapless performs miracles. He wrestles with the steering wheel and manages amazingly, to stop the minibus from crashing. It comes to an uncertain halt facing the wrong way.

"That Teddy Toxic is a maniac!" screams Mr Hapless. "I'm going to run down to the village and get the police."

"But Sir," cries your friend, Satinda, out loud, "You're rubbish at running! Don't you remember the obstacle race?"

"Ah, yes, all right Sandy,"

"It's Satinda, Sir"

"OK Satinda, you run as fast as you can to the police station and tell them what's happened."

Go to 183.

172 If you chose code 008, go to 198.
If you chose code 504, go to 184.
If you chose any other code, go to 159.

173 You start running back down the
corridor to try and join the school group.
You hear footsteps from around the corner of the
corridor. As a figure starts to emerge, you begin
blurting out your excuse.

"I'm sorry, Mr Hapless, I thought I saw a burglar
running down the corridors. I gave chase but I lost
him. He had a stripey shirt and a big sack with
swag written on his..." You stop dead.

The footsteps didn't belong to Mr Hapless, they
belonged to Teddy Toxic.

"Hello, hello, what do we have here then?" asks
Toxic with an evil grin.

You're in deep trouble.

Go to 77.

174 The platform keeps crumbling, but
Toxman's increased speed from the
power pill keeps him just ahead. Suddenly, the
platform stops crumbling. Toxman is safe. Phew!

Looking at the screen, you can see a choice, an
up and a down ladder. You glance at the screen
clock. There are just ten seconds left, so you'll
have to hurry.

**Do you want to guide Toxman down (go to 150)
or up (go to 190)?**

175 You enter with relief what looks like a normal, modern room. You shut the door carefully behind you.

"Hello Meddler!" It's Teddy Toxic with two fierce-looking dogs.

Go to 196.

176 You keep on running, even though your legs really ache and your lungs are bursting. Rounding a bend, you slip and fall. From around the corner comes that familiar engine noise. Teddy Toxic has tracked you down again. The jeep, engine revving hard, is heading straight for you. Suddenly, an arm clamps itself on your shoulders. You feel yourself being sharply pulled back on to the pavement.

"What do you think you're playing at?" It's PC Coppit. Teddy Toxic's jeep roars by and disappears into the distance. You're safe.

"Are you OK?"

"Yes, officer, I'm fine," you manage to say in between breaths. "I've got to get home. I'm late for my favourite cartoon show. I've just twisted my ankle a bit, that's all."

"Well, if you're sure that you're all right?"

"Yes, I'm fine."

"OK then, off you go and be more careful on the road in future."

Relieved that the policeman saved you from Toxic, you quickly head home.

Go to 129.

177 The screen flashes black and white as a gloomy tune is played through the computer speaker. Game Over appears on the screen.

If you've played the game twice, go to 147, otherwise go to 155.

178 "Have you got the comic, issue 219?"
"Y...y...yes," you stutter.

"Good, as you can see I've got the, uh, trousers you want. Let's trade."

Feeling very nervous, you walk towards Toxic

and his hell hounds. You both stretch out your arms. Toxic grabs the comic and starts stroking the cover. You grab the trousers and fold them up.

Meanwhile, in the centre of the village, the strangest creature ever to visit Eldon is slowly making its way through the empty streets.

"So we're off to the wasteland just outside Eldon. It's lucky we intercepted that message before it reached the kid."

"Shut up and stop jiggling about."

Go to 96.

179 There's a knock at the front door. You open the door and see Inspector Marchbank from Eldon police station. She invites herself in.

She looks ever so uncomfortable. "What's the matter?" you ask.

"Er, well this is very difficult for me..."

"What is?"

The Inspector takes a deep breath, "Oh well, here goes. We, the police, were wrong and you, a mere child, were right. We now believe that Teddy Toxic was behind the water pollution."

You sit down, amazed. "What changed your mind?"

"The fact, that after everyone moved, Toxic has started planning to knock down the whole village."

"He can't do that," you gasp.

"Oh, he can. Remember, he owns it now. We tapped his telephone and caught a conversation between him and a major criminal. They were laughing about what he'd done."

"Wow!" you exclaim.

"We think we need a little more evidence before we can swoop and arrest him. We need any help that you can give us about the ToxCo Complex or those toxic trousers of his. Will you help us?" the Inspector pleads.

"Yes, of course," you cry out loud. "Maybe Eldon can be saved after all."

THE END

180 Toxman swallows the power pill and continues running. The platform behind him starts crumbling. You push the joystick as hard as you can. Beads of sweat start appearing on your forehead because of all your concentration. Will Toxman make it?

Remove the power pill from your list and go to 174.

181 Toxman runs straight into an Ecotrap. "Aaaarrrgghhh!" the computer speaker sounds. Toxman falls down and dissolves from the screen. Oh no!

Go to 177.

182 You creep through the door into the room called The Inner Sanctum. Wow! In the middle of this high tech building, Toxic has a room shaped just like the *Death Cave* in the Biceps Man comic.

Faint noises in the distance stop you from gazing around for too long. What should you do now? There's nothing much in this room apart from a rope hanging down, a wooden chest and another door on the far side of the stone room.

Go to 140.

183 Relieved that everyone in the minibus is OK, you continue running, but you've lost precious time. You speed down along the track and into the village as fast as you can. You make it to the village centre but the roar of the jeep engine makes it clear that Teddy Toxic is not far behind.

Leaning on a pillar box while you catch your breath, you try to decide what to do next. The roar of Teddy Toxic's jeep is getting closer and closer. "Quick, think!" you say to yourself.

Do you go over to the police station (go to 189)?
Do you go over to the offices of the *Eldon Gazette* (go to 122)?
Do you throw the package in the hedge (go to 89)?
Do you put the package in the post box (go to 195)?

184 The computer whirrs into life. Wow! The code you just entered has put you on the final screen. Up flashes a map of the whole final screen. You get a short look at it before the game starts again.

Count to ten as you look at the game screen below and then quickly go to 115.

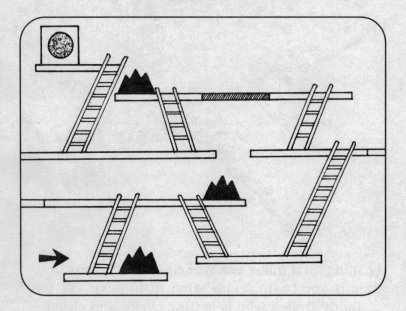

185 Teddy Toxic quickly catches you. "Pesky kid," he hisses, shaking you up and down until you feel quite sick. He grabs the envelope containing the photo and trousers and throws you to the floor. He bends down towards you, his fists clenched and the veins in his forehead throbbing with anger. You've never felt so frightened before.

You hear a shout from Satinda in the distance. Toxic jerks upright with a start.

"Damn, I don't want witnesses," he snarls, stomping off to his jeep. He starts the engine running and races away.

"Are you OK?" gasps Satinda. "Yes, I think you've just saved me," you reply, still trembling.

"Not from Mr Hapless though," adds Satinda, spotting Mr Hapless walking fiercely towards you.

Go to 129.

186 Along the platform Toxman rushes until he arrives at a long ladder. You guide Toxman up the ladder.

As he reaches the top of the ladder, the clock shows just three seconds. Toxman is now on a new platform level.

Go to 188.

187 What's this? An enormous figure, three metres high, stands in front of you. In the night-time gloom you struggle to make out who or what it is. It looks strangely familiar. Teddy Toxic recognises it just before you do.

"Biceps Man!" he screams, quaking with fear. "Yes, it is I, Biceps Man, sworn enemy of evil throughout the galaxy," roars the huge figure.

Teddy Toxic falls to his knees.

"Hand over the trousers, Toxic, or it'll be curtains for you."

"But if I do, I'll be, I'll be, uh, ruined," Toxic protests, shivering with fright.

"Do as I say or you will taste the awesome might of my Fist of Fear!" Biceps Man booms.

Teddy Toxic wimpers and drops the brightly patterned trousers to the ground. You quickly gather the trousers into your hands just as Teddy Toxic bursts into tears.

"Now take this evidence to the police, child," says Biceps Man. "And as for you Toxic, you run home to your ToxCo complex and stay there."

"B…b…but," Toxic snivels.

"Do as I say, or by thunder, I will thwhack you into infinity," Biceps Man roars. Toxic squeals in fear and starts running.

Add the toxic trousers to your list and go to 92.

188 The screen shows the giant button ahead and just two seconds remaining on the clock. As quick as a flash, you push Toxman into the button. All action stops. Did you make it in time or did the clock run out? The computer pauses for a moment.

Go to 162.

189 You head for the safety of the police station but it's on the other side of the main road. Teddy Toxic's jeep is roaring down the road. He cuts you off before you reach the station. You try to dodge but it's no use. Teddy Toxic has you cornered.

Go to 185.

190 Toxman runs along the platform. The screen clock shows that there are eight seconds remaining.

Go to 148.

191 As you rush round a dark corner, you bump into some iron railings and drop the envelope. Bending down to pick up the package, you curse. The roar of the jeep's engine is now very, very close.

Go to 185.

192 Inspector Marchbank comes to join PC Coppit at the front desk.

"What's going on?" she says scowling. You breathlessly explain everything that you've learnt in your adventures. When you've finished, she turns to you and leans over the desk.

"What does this badge say?"

"Detective Inspector," you reply.

"So, leave the detective work to me," she snaps.

"But the Eco Warriors…"

"Enough of the Eco Warriors, you shouldn't be messing around with them. In fact, I think your parents should know. PC Coppit?"

"Yes Madam."

"Take this child back home to Bridge Street and explain what's been happening. I'll return these trousers to Mr Toxic with an apology," says the Inspector.

Go to 108.

193 You don't have enough evidence against Teddy Toxic. The trousers remain safely in Teddy Toxic's hands. There's no way around it. You've tried hard but you failed.

You're not surprised when, a short while later, you spot the front page of the *Swallowtown Weekly* newspaper which has replaced the closed-down *Eldon Gazette*. Teddy Toxic has really won.

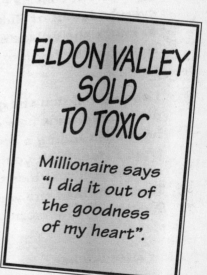

ELDON VALLEY SOLD TO TOXIC

Millionaire says "I did it out of the goodness of my heart".

THE END

194

You hear a rattle at the door and the sound of something hitting the doormat. You wander through and pick up the letter. It's addressed to you. Hopefully, Rob, Satinda or one of your other friends has written to you.

You rip open the envelope and unfold the letter.

2 The Lane
Emdon

Hi there,

It took me ages to track you down to your new home. I'm afraid Teddy Toxic has been up to his evil tricks again. Now, that he's managed to turf everybody out of Eldon, he's planning to knock the village down and turn the whole valley into one gigantic car park.

I should tell you the good news. I discovered some new evidence while I have been hiding a few miles away from Eldon. With your help, I think we can still convince the Police that Toxic poisoned the water. I'll be in Swallowtown tomorrow to discuss plans.

Best Wishes

Doug 'Deadline' Dennis,
Ex-Editor of the Ex-Eldon Gazette

"Here we go again," you cry, waving the letter in the air. "We'll get you this time, Teddy Toxic!"

THE END

---

195 You push the padded envelope into the postbox's slot and start running again. Toxic's jeep slows down as it passes through the village centre and then speeds up again to chase you.

Go to 74.

196 "B-b-but I thought you were away on business," you gasp in horror.

"That's what I told everyone, so that I could work undisturbed. I'd forgotten about your school trip, however," he replies. "Now, I suggest you put back anything you've taken before I set these dogs on to you. They haven't eaten properly since my last hit single."

"But that must have been…"

"Yes, many years ago," Teddy Toxic interrupts, smiling his gruesome smile and showing his gold teeth. A shiver runs down your spine. You're trapped.

Toxic takes his things from you and cackles. "Now, let's get you back to your stupid school group."

If you had the trousers, remove them from your list.
Go to 77.

197 You endure an uneasy evening watching the television with your family. Nine o'clock approaches and your mum and stepdad have started arguing about moving out of Eldon. Perfect timing. You manage to slip out of the house while they quarrel.

You make your way to the wasteland outside the centre of the village. It was dark and quiet in the village and you didn't see a soul. This wasteland looks just as deserted.

"Maybe it was just a joke," you say out loud.

"No joke, kid. I can, uh, assure you of, uh, that." Teddy Toxic steps out of the shadows and you gasp. In one hand, he's carrying the toxic trousers, but in his other hand he holds two leads, attached to the collars of the most ferocious-looking dogs you've ever seen.

Go to 178.

198 Up comes the game screen. You see a map of the whole screen then the game shows you the view ahead through the eyes of the game's character, Toxman.

Grabbing the computer's joystick, you start to play. You have to guide Toxman up and down ladders and along platforms. You start well, stamping on some flowers to gain points, and avoiding some obvious traps. You zap a scientist and jump on to the second screen.

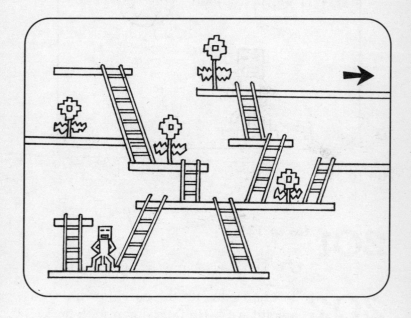

"Excellent," you whisper to yourself.

Go to 165.

199 If you picked track 1, go to 93, otherwise go to 124.

200 You start up your stepdad's computer and pop in the blue disk. Clicking on the one file that the disk contains, the computer displays a bright screen. You don't believe it. It's the infamous Toxman game!

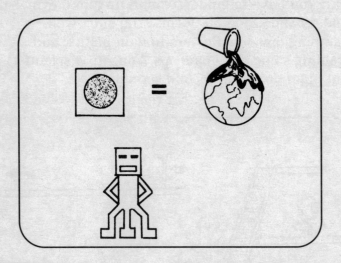

Go to 134.

201 Go to 139.

202 Toxman runs up the corridor and into a solid wall. He falls down with a bump. "Ouch!" squeals the computer speaker. However much you move the joystick, the evil little creature won't get up. "Come on, come on!" you urge it.

Go to 126.

MISSION LIST

Use this page to keep a record of any objects
you carry with you.

Your two birthday comics
90p

MISSION LIST

Use this page to keep a record of any objects
you carry with you.

Your two birthday comics
90p

MISSION LIST

Use this page to keep a record of any objects
you carry with you.

Your two birthday comics
90p

PLOTBUSTERS

THE

COSMIC

TOASTER

It's the 23rd century and the High Priestess of
the Solar System is hungry.
"I'm fed up of Plutoburgers and astro salads!"
her Imperial Greatness screams. "I want a
good old-fashioned Earth breakfast with lots
of TOAST!"

Five nanoseconds later you're hurtling
through space to find the only remaining
toaster in the galaxy.

Will you bring it safely back to Her Royal
Hungryness? Or face a lifetime of mopping the
palace kitchen floor?

PLOTBUSTERS

The Really Useless SPY SCHOOL

Your talent for skulduggery is just what The
Really Useless Spy School needs.

You're assigned an important secret mission:
someone has stolen the Prime Minister's wig
and he's refusing to leave home without it!

Can you rescue the wig in time for the PM to
sign the World Peace Agreement? Or will the
dastardly villains take over the world?

PLOTBUSTERS

UNCLE ALF
AND THE
TIME TRAVEL
DETECTIVES

Uncle Alf, an ex-inventor, has been sacked from his job as a museum security guard. A dinosaur bone was stolen while he was on duty!

If you can fix one of his old inventions, you'll be able to travel back in time to find another bone, so Alf can get his job back.

That's if you don't get arrested by a Victorian policeman, trapped in an Egyptian pyramid, or run over by Roman charioteers...

ORDER FORM

65595 X	THE REALLY USELESS SPY SCHOOL Clive Gifford	£3.99	☐
65593 3	THE COSMIC TOASTER Clive Gifford	£3.99	☐
65594 1	UNCLE ALF AND THE TIME TRAVEL DETECTIVES Clive Gifford	£3.99	☐

All Hodder Children's books are available at your local bookshop or newsagent, or can be ordered direct from the publisher.
Just tick the titles you want and fill in the form below.
Prices and availability subject to change without notice.

Hodder Children's Books, Cash Sales Department, Bookpoint, 39 Milton Park, Abingdon, OXON OX14 4TD, UK. If you have a credit card you may order by telephone - 01235 831700.

Please enclose a cheque or postal order made payable to Bookpoint Ltd to the value of the cover price and allow the following for postage and packing:
UK & BFPO: £1.00 for the first book, 50p for the second book and 30p for each additional book ordered up to a maximum charge of £3.00. OVERSEAS & EIRE: £2.00 for the first book, £1.00 for the second book and 50p for each additional book.

Name ....

Address ....

....

....

If you would prefer to pay by credit card, please complete:
Please debit my Visa/Access/Diner's Card/American Express (delete as applicable) card no:

Signature ....

Expiry Date ....